Praise for Mon

MW00769865

"When I learned that my ...... and colleague, Megan Weigel, had created a collection of Monday Mantras, I was eager to read the reflections coming out of her year of introspection and her process of personal healing and growth. I wanted to experience her generous gift to others who are working toward their own emotional and physical wellness. I am a psychologist whose work is closely aligned with Megan's – focused on the emotional well-being of individuals living with chronic illness. Even with years of professional work behind me, I was drawn into this small but weighty collection of insights into the pressures and intensity of our lives – of my life. I found myself reading every page and identifying with the messages that somehow seemed to talk directly to me, my past and present.

Whether you are looking for ideas to stimulate your own introspection, accompany your meditation practice, guide your yoga practice, or learn about the properties of essential oils, I urge you to take this book to a quiet space and use it in whatever way feels right to you. However you use it, you will find Megan there to support you."

-Rosalind Kalb, PhD,
Senior Consultant, Can Do Multiple Sclerosis,
author of *Multiple Sclerosis for Dummies* and
*Multiple Sclerosis: The Questions You Have;
The Answers You Need*

"Monday Mantras with Megan will provide a soothing balm for a harried soul, whether the stress is from normal day-to-day living or from a chronic illness. Unlike most books that can be read just once and set aside, Monday Mantras with Megan is a book that keeps giving fresh insights on reducing stress and enjoying life. I find that with each reading of her book, I incorporate more of the stress-reducing and healing methods that she mentions. It is truly a worthwhile investment, and each short chapter can be read and implemented, even with the most hectic schedule."

-Melissa Main, author of *Impossible Quest: One Man's Journey for Adventure on the Last Frontier*

"Megan Weigel is not only a brilliant and deeply caring neurology Nurse Practitioner, she is also a yoga teacher and an Integrative Medicine fellowship graduate. Her Monday Mantras are a perfect tool to improve your well-being one heartfelt and doable step at a time!"

-Victoria Maizes, MD,
Andrew Weil Endowed Chair in Integrative Medicine
and Executive Director, Andrew Weil
Center for Integrative Medicine;
Professor of Clinical Medicine, Family Medicine
and Public Health, University of Arizona

"Monday Mantras with Megan is an inspiring book you'll turn to again and again. I know I do. Megan's advice is commonsensical and calming, infused with her hard-won wisdom, unique perspective, and sweet soul. The mantras are little works of art operating on the levels of the mind, body, and spirit. I am grateful for her guidance...and the reminder to be still."

-Nancy Monson, writer, artist, health coach, and
author of *Craft to Heal: Soothing Your Soul
with Sewing, Painting,* and *Other Pastimes*

"In this fast-paced world, we forget to slow down and appreciate life, especially during difficult times. We forget the importance of self-care, and the well runs dry. Megan shares this simple and easy-to-follow companion for daily meditation that will guide you back into your body and away from overwhelm.

Megan combines inspired, daily thoughts and actions you can use to remember who you are. Easy yoga movements help to ground you and bring you back to your center. Your sense of smell is activated through the use of different healing oils to help integrate this mindful experience. Monday Mantras with Megan reminds you to breathe and brings you into the moment where you are most powerful."

-Maren Nelson, Master Teacher of Breathwork,
author of *Ride the Emotional Wave*

Monday Mantras with Megan

Weekly Intentions for Enjoying Your Journey

Megan R. Weigel

Hardcover: ISBN 979-8-9854687-1-7
Paperback: ISBN 979-8-9854687-0-0
Ebook: ISBN 979-8-9854687-2-4

Library of Congress Control Number: 2022914866

First paperback edition September 2022
1. HEALTH & FITNESS / Holism. 2. BODY, MIND & SPIRIT / Mindfulness & Meditation. 3. SELF-HELP / Self-Management / Stress Management

Inside Biography Photograph by Rob Futrell

Back Cover Photograph by Corinna Hoffman Photography

Published by First Coast Integrative Medicine
Jacksonville Beach, Florida

www.mondaymantraswithmegan.com

Table of Contents

Welcome

Dear Friend,

Thank you for choosing this little book to be a part of your week. Your mind, body, and soul thank you, too.

I started writing and recording these mantras the first Monday of 2020, unaware of what would follow as the year geared up. Let's just say that, even without a global pandemic, my amusement park of a life that I dared to share in the form of lessons, let gos, and let ins seemed to resonate. Each week, many people reached out to tell me just how timely that Monday Mantra was for them as they experienced what can only be likened to "ripping the Band-Aid right off."

Guess what? Wounds need air to heal, so somehow the timing was right. Monday Mantras were, and still are, helping people heal.

I am not a guru. I have been a nurse practitioner in neurology for more than a couple of decades now, as well as a student of neuroscience and integrative medicine and a specialist in the field of multiple sclerosis (MS). I care for people who face hard things as soon as they open their eyes in the morning. In 2012, I had the serendipitous experience of completing a yoga teacher training and beginning to teach yoga to people living with MS. At the same time, I invited that yoga to heal my mind and heart through my body. I have been on a personal healing journey for more than 10 years, emotionally and physically, using yoga, prayer, mindfulness, and energy medicine. These Monday Mantras, though? I'm quite sure they began when I started collecting quotes as a pre-teen and using them to help me make it through tough times. These mantras come from so many disciplines and schools of thought, and ultimately, from my heart to yours.

What is a mantra?

A mantra is a word or series of words used to help meditation along. The science of mindfulness and meditation tells us wonderful things about their benefits, but so many people either don't know where to start OR don't start because they say:

I don't have enough time.

I can't shut off my brain.

I can't sit still.

I don't like apps.

It seems so hard.

What if I don't do it right?

Why should I do this? And why on MONDAYS?

Mindfulness practices like meditation and breathwork offer low-hanging fruit to boost well-being even with a simple practice: They are associated with scientifically proven benefits for relieving anxiety and depression, raising awareness of one's own feelings, and improving non-judgmental acceptance. They can also help to improve pain and heart health and lessen susceptibility to infection, as well as heighten cognitive function and focus. It's been shown that longer periods and practice of meditation actually cause positive changes in neural networks in the brain and in brain structure!

We also know that micro-dosing meditation works.

Slowing down and deepening your breath for just 2 minutes works.

Try it now. I'm serious. Stop what you are doing. Set a timer for 2 minutes and take slow deep breaths in and out to a count of 4 or 5.

How do you feel?

Yep, you experienced it!

On Mondays, more than needing one more thing to DO, we need things to NOT do. Use your Monday Mantra as a gift to NOT do something. You could tell yourself:

"I will not be as worried."

"I will not be as negative."

"I will not be as frightened."

"I will not be as stressed."

"I will not overfill."

Each of us has a cup that we hold and can handle. Our cups fill with all sorts of exposures and stuff as we get older: illnesses, traumas, toxins, crappy food, bad air, toxic stress. These things are chronically inflammatory to our bodies—and inflammation is bad for our health. There will come a point when your cup will overflow or even tip over if all you do is put stuff in it. Overflow looks like a breakdown, a major medical illness, a smoldering problem that finally gets your attention, or any number of other life-altering events.

You should practice Monday Mantras because mindfulness is like a release valve on your cup. It will help you empty your cup so you can fill it up with new and better things.

How should I use this guide?

Each week, you will be presented with a mantra and an activity to support that mantra for the week.

Ways to use the mantras:

The Way of the Peaceful Warrior

-Set a timer once a day for 2-5 minutes.

-Sit in a quiet, comfortable place and gently close your eyes.

-See or say the mantra to yourself as you breathe in and out a little more slowly and deeply than usual.

-Gently open your eyes and get up, feeling relaxed and rejuvenated.

Stop, Drop, and Roll

-Write the mantra on a few sticky notes and place the notes in conspicuous places (bathroom mirror, refrigerator, car dashboard, computer screen, etc.).

-Every time you see one, give it a nod, stop what you are doing, and take a deep breath.

-Then resume going about your business.

Some helpful suggestions for mindfulness and meditation:

1. Keep it simple.

2. Don't judge how well you are doing at meditation. Just do it.

3. Don't set yourself up for failure. I suppose I could say set yourself up for success, but that seems to make people try too hard.

4. If you have a hard time sitting still or have never practiced meditation, start with 1-2 minutes on the timer.

5. If you miss a day, don't give up. Meditation is the practice of beginning again—and again. Just try again tomorrow until you develop a rhythm.

<u>Ways to use the activities:</u>

Each week is associated with an activity, represented by an icon. These activities are meant to encourage you to try something simple that invites more positivity into your life. Some weeks, you may just do the activity once; other weeks, you may find you are doing it daily. There should be no judgement attached to how you use the activity because we all have different opportunities of time, likes, and dislikes, and these may change daily.

The activities will rotate in the same order throughout the weeks in the following categories:

MOVEMENT

A suggestion to move the body using a yoga pose.

MINDFULNESS

A tip on how to be more in the moment. Mindfulness suggestions may include different types of breathing exercises or instructions for doing things you do every day, but with more presence.

COLOR

This activity focuses on "see-through objects"—things we no longer notice because we see them every day. Color suggestions may come in the form of eating a rainbow of foods, pursuing creative activities, wearing a new color, or simply focusing on something we see frequently and looking at it in a new way.

ESSENTIAL OIL

Scents can be powerful relaxants and energizers. I will recommend diffusing essential oils* based on the mood of each mantra.

Essential oil safety is important. Never ingest (swallow) or apply essential oils to the body without direction from a person who is well-versed in their use. Choose a reputable brand such as Doterra® or Young Living™, or check with your local health food store for brands that are organic and free of chemicals.

Enjoy the Journey

These are your Monday Mantras, and this is your journey with them. I believe in being honest and realistic: Some weeks will be more difficult than others. I have learned the things I least want to sit with are often the ones I need to sit with the longest.

If you come across a week that generates some resistance, be gentle with yourself, but stay with it. One of the reasons I chose to make these weekly is because ah-hah moments in healing often occur days after you've heard or read or experienced something.

Many weeks will be fun! You will nod "yes" as you read the mantra and accompanying text, you will feel supported and in good company, and the activity will support that release.

Enjoy. Give yourself grace and gratitude for beginning, and for beginning again.

Blessings,

Megan

"And the end of all our exploring will be to arrive where we started and know the place for the first time."

T.S. Eliot

Week 1

I relax into new beginnings.

The new year is historically a time for reset. It is a time for giving up old behaviors that did not cause personal growth, setting resolutions to create a positive future, and resetting negative thinking. Nonetheless, many of us race into the new year with tough goals instead of achievable ones. In the past we may have given up early, or worse, dug ourselves into the "this will never happen for me" hole.

According to ancient practices of Chinese medicine and Ayurveda, winter is a time to turn inward, practice self-reflection, sleep a little more, and nourish yourself. This is the exact opposite of many of the resolutions we rush out the door with on New Year's Day...exercise more, start a challenging

program, meet financial goals, lose 15 pounds...
and we expect to be complete by January 15!

Relaxing into new beginnings is simply a suggestion
to give yourself grace in your goals as well as time
to notice their true meaning in your life.

The movement of healing occurs in stillness. Lie on your back with your arms at your sides, palms facing up. Let your feet relax. Close your eyes. This is *savasana*, also called *corpse pose* or *final rest*, and it is an actual yoga pose. It is a handoff from busy body and brain to stillness. Relax.

Week 2

I find calm with my breath.

When situations go awry, or I find myself becoming anxious, I turn to breath. Currently, I do this almost unconsciously, but it took a lot of work. Sometimes it still takes a lot of work! If I don't go right to breath, then I notice my neck muscles are tight, my brow is wrinkled, my heart is racing, and my mind is not kind to me. Breath fixes all of that.

When was the last time you felt anxious? Maybe your caseload for the day was high. Maybe you were waiting for a call or a test result. Think of how it felt. Now, take a slow deep breath in. Let it fill you up from front to back, side to side, and bottom to top. Allow an even slower exhale, 2-3 seconds longer than your inhale (studies show that a longer exhale reminds your brain to stay calm). Next time you are faced with stress, can you try a deep breath instead of your old pattern?

This is a cleansing breath. A sigh without a sigh. Sit comfortably wherever you are. You don't even have to close your eyes. Breathe in, then breathe out completely. Next, breathe in through your nose to a count of 4, open your mouth, and exhale through your mouth to a count of 6. Smile. Repeat.

Week 3

My work becomes easier when I smile.

I had no idea how much of the day I spent with my brow furrowed until it wasn't anymore. I truthfully did not notice the daily tension headache until it was gone. Life shouldn't be lived like that! On this day, I am blessed to do the work God put me here to do. It is hard work. Each day, it challenges my mind, heart, and soul—even the budgeting of my time. But it is my purpose, and for that, I smile.

When I smile, my forehead and ears and jaw relax. When I smile my shoulders fall away from my ears, and I sit up taller. When I smile, the hard work becomes easier, and I have energy to continue. When I smile, I connect with others and days are bright. Something tells me your daily work is similar. Try to smile more this week, or as I like to say, "Try on more smiling this week."

To accompany your bright smile, wear something yellow this week. It is the color of happiness, optimism, and your solar plexus or energy center. Buy a bright bunch of yellow flowers and set them on your desk or kitchen table as a mantra reminder.

Week 4

I can rely on my memory.

Alright, this is a biggie. In the era of the 3rd hand called the Smart Phone, many of us just write everything down—not because we have to, but because we can! A couple of the reasons I hear the most for whipping out the Notes app or a list are, "I have so much going on, I'm afraid I will forget it!" OR "Well, I'm always multi-tasking, so I can't remember anything."

Listen. Anxiety, pain, and memory compete for the same highway in the brain, and *memory* ALWAYS LOSES. And guess what? This leads to slews of healthy people worried about early dementia or major health crises.

The solution? Practice. Exercise your memory.

Trust that it works. Take it out for a little dance this week, give it some fresh air, and believe in yourself. Even if you do have to write things down because of a medical condition, I encourage you to try this exercise and create some new connections in your brain.

Spearmint and rosemary essential oils may help with focus and memory. Place a few drops of each in a diffuser and turn on while working or reading this week.

Week 5

My voice is heard and my words are worthwhile.

How many of us wonder if what we have to say is worthwhile? Will people wonder what the heck we are thinking, get upset, or even question our abilities if we share our ideas or thoughts? Similarly, are you quiet because at some point in your life, you didn't feel heard? Because of past programming, we stay silent when there are words and ideas on our hearts that are screaming to be shared.

This week's work is to let it sink in that your voice is a valuable part of a shared song. And maybe, just maybe, share your first verse.

From a kneeling position, come to tabletop, or all-fours, by dropping the palms of your hands to the floor in front of you so you have a flat back. You are starting *Cat-Cow pose*, or *marjaryasana bitilasana*. Your knees are directly under your hips and your wrists are lined up under your shoulders as the palms of your hands press into the ground. As you inhale, lift your tailbone so your belly drops towards the floor and look up to the ceiling, extending through your neck. As you exhale, tuck your chin and arch your back, tucking your tailbone. Repeat this 3 times. Among its many benefits, including warming up the spine, this pose helps to clear your throat chakra.

Week 6

I am not missing out when I put my phone down.

Reluctantly, I am on social media because of my integrative medicine practice. Sometimes I want to throw my phone into the ocean. One of the worst feelings I've felt recently was when my toddler son yelled at me, "Mommy, put your phone down!" We were playing outside, and I stopped because I felt like I had a free minute to post something that might benefit the practice…which means get more likes, get more followers, get more business…but at the expense of my family?

No thanks. I don't want that to be the memory my son has of me. I know I am not the only one who is saddened to look around a restaurant and see no one talking (of any age group!) because everyone is staring at their phones.

Folks. Put your phone down. You are missing out on connection—the sunrise, the sunset, the rainbow, the smile . . . all right in front of you NOW. We all need a break during these crazy times of being constantly available and accessible. If someone doesn't call you back fast enough, you text. If they don't email you fast enough, you send an instant message. This is an easy message to take. Take it with some breaths…and give those you are trying to reach the chance to take some breaths, too.

The next time you pick up your phone or tablet because you have a free moment, pause. Why are you choosing to pick up your device? Close your eyes and take a couple of deep and clearing breaths as you examine your choice. Social media and surfing the internet are things that give us little shots of dopamine. After your pause, if you decide that is what you want, go for it! But maybe you will decide to take more deep breaths, hug a loved one, or dance to your favorite song instead.

Week 7

Worry does not serve me.

I have a dear friend who epitomizes joy. She is always positive, and I look to her for that sunshine when I need it. She said to me the other day, "Did you know that worry is the opposite of prayer?" What a novel, and true, concept! In fact, a few months ago, I sent myself an email that said, "I will not worry for 30 days." Once I deleted emails for the day, it was always at the top of my Inbox. And guess what? It worked. I might START to worry, but then I would see the little reminder. I would then say a prayer instead of worrying.

This week, write yourself a note or email that says, "I will not worry this week." You may find your concerns become tasks that get done, instead of things that do you in.

Treat yourself to a box of Crayola crayons, the one with 64 colors. Choose colors that you associate with joy and freedom and create your "I will not worry this week" page.

Week 8

Ho'oponopono

To make right…with self and others; ho-oponopono is the Hawaiian practice of forgiving oneself and others. The process includes repentance, forgiveness, gratitude and love. You take responsibility for your actions as well as the actions of others and cut *aka* connections. Aka connections energetically hold the preconceptions you've held in your relationships. You might think, why would I want to take responsibility for something someone else did to me? Well, that person may not be capable of taking the responsibility…and you are both deserving of healing.

"You are absolutely free when you have no data points," said Ihaleakala Hew Len, PhD, a master teacher of the work. You get a blank canvas.

The rhythm of ho-oponopono includes the phrases: "I am sorry. Please forgive me. Thank you. I love you."

Try it this week with a person who has you stuck in a negative emotional pattern. Close your eyes. Calm your breath. See that person. Say with intention, "I am sorry. Please forgive me. Thank you. I love you."

Place a few drops of bergamot in your diffuser as you practice the rhythm of ho-oponopono. Let the aroma help you release and feel empowered to practice forgiveness.

Week 9

I need rest to thrive.

After making it through a busy weekend filled with extra speaking engagements, plus all the usual weekend chores, I looked in the mirror and saw a haggard-looking human staring back at me. I found my temper short, and I was hungry for rest. I had a stark realization that, even though I love what I do, I need rest if I don't want resentment to develop.

My interpersonal work is to realize the importance of choosing my yeses so that I can put energy where I need it most and be my best self. I need rest to thrive. This might mean I go home early if my work is done in the office, or I cut a workout short, or I choose sleep. It might mean I say no to a social engagement in order to play with my family, or I set limits with my ego-self on working after hours and on weekends.

This week, choose extra rest. Let your mind and body know that the default mode does not have to be overdrive. You will find you cultivate better inner soil.

From a kneeling position, come forward onto your hands and knees. Bring your big toes to touch, keeping your knees wide. Sink your hips back towards your heels as you reach your arms forward, allowing your chest and head to come towards the mat. Let your forehead rest on the mat. As you inhale, stretch your arms forward on the ground, and as you exhale try to sink your hips that have come off your heels back towards them. *Child's pose (balasana)* releases tension and helps relieve anxiety.

Week 10

I make room for good thoughts to root and grow in my heart and mind.

Thoughts are like food. If we eat the ones that are rotten, or that we know make us feel badly, we can expect a bellyache at the very least. Like food, we get to choose what thoughts we let into our minds.

There is quite a bit of discord in the world right now. The best we can do is arm ourselves with reliable sources of information to make sound decisions and be kind to one another. Once we do that, it is our individual responsibility to make room for good thoughts to root and grow in our hearts and minds. It is only in making that room that we can cultivate well-being and healing for ourselves and others.

The thoughts we let into our hearts and minds can cause diseases similar to those caused by poor nutrition. Think about that. This week, look for positive and kind words to fill your head and heart.

Try a new practice: heart-centered breathing. Close your eyes and begin to breathe a little more slowly and deeply than usual, without straining. Once you feel comfortable with that rhythm, imagine that your breath is coming in and going out through your heart center. This may literally be the left-side of your chest, or the center of your chest. Breathe positivity in through your heart center on the inhale and send positivity back to the world through your heart center as you exhale.

Week II

Hope does not disappoint.

I wrote this mantra after several days of taking frenzied phone calls from halfway across the world, getting little and sleep to rise and create online content, consult with patients, and help my yoga studio develop a prevention policy. And all the while, I felt a sense of calm. This is what I wrote the week that COVID-19 became a frightening international pandemic while we were on our yearly trip to Haleiwa:

Well, there has been a drastic change of events in the past week...of such an effect that I never thought we would see this outside the movie theater. Call me naïve if you'd like, as many have said they can't believe a viral crisis like this took so long. I'll take my position at the podium of realism.

It may sound like pessimism to some, but to me it means I believe in science and faith. It is going to be a harrowing time. But, I cannot help but know deep in my being that there is a reason for this. And while it may be beyond my understanding, it is not beyond my inner knowing. So, I have hope.

I listened to Mass yesterday, and the second reading was Romans 5:3-5: "...where there is tribulation, there is perseverance; and perseverance, character; and character, hope...and hope does not disappoint."

We flew home across the Pacific the week that COVID-19 started to shut down airports and countries. We left our second home of safe, simple and sacred space with Clorox wipes and masks to get on jumbo airliners and travel overnight through empty airports. We made it safely. We were ready to face our next steps with hope because the other choices just weren't sustainable. Hope is always available. Grab a corner of it. It will grow in you.

Cliché of the day: It takes both rain and sunshine to make a rainbow. Grab that box of crayons again, and draw a rainbow, one of the most common symbols of hope.

Week 12

What can I give up today?

This week's mantra is not a statement to consider, but a daily call to action. We don't usually ask ourselves to give things up; we usually challenge ourselves to take things on. In taking things on, we take on excitement, planning for the unknown, and expectation. If those goals are not fulfilled in our timeline, the associated emotions can become heaviness or sadness; a sense of loss; lack of support or fear. Most of us have had to face some dark emotions recently, and many have found this has opened up space for the light.

Each day this week, ask yourself, "What can I give up today?" so that you make room for more light. Today, I give up judging my success by checked boxes in my planner. Hell, today, I give up my daily plan. Sheesh…writing those words makes my skin crawl…but deeper underneath, I feel a sense of relief and lightness. What if I didn't get all the things done, and we all survived another day?

Get into those dark and dusty corners. Let the light in to shake up the dust and wake up your soul. It is messy and uncomfortable, but oh, is it necessary. What can you give up today?

Diffuse sandalwood essential oil this week for balance.

Week 13

I remember all the people who loved me.

The scene in the movie *A Beautiful Day in the Neighborhood* that struck me most was when Mr. Rogers asked someone to think of all the people who had loved him into being. A montage of interviews followed.

There are times in our lives when we are forced to be away from others. For some it is a deadline, for others an illness; maybe your job or duty takes you away. Of course, death separates us. But being apart in physical space does not change the strength of the influence of people who have loved you "into being". Feeling this gives fuel for the heart and creates space for healing.

Take some moments each day to remember the

people near and far, with us here on earth and who have passed, who have loved you into being. If there is no immediate visceral connection to this loving energy, then think of the people who shifted your shape and changed your heart, mind, or soul; the people who gave time to you; the people who nurtured you and allowed you to grow; the people who taught you, coached you, led you.

The emotions that you feel as you do this are just more affirmation that we are all connected—that the energy they gave or still give to you is able to be used for your highest good.

How do you feel in your body when you consider all the people who love(d) you?

From a kneeling position, come to all fours, or tabletop. Tuck your toes and send your hips high so that you are an inverted V. This is *downward facing dog* or *adho mukha savasana.* Press your palms into the floor, and relax your head and chest so they shift through your arms. Pull your belly in and up towards your spine. Play with bending your knees a tiny bit or raising up and down on your toes. If your heels are touching the floor, walk your feet back a little more so they don't. Feel your body awaken to movement.

Week 14

What is now for me?

One day I was running and found myself praying about what was next for me. I was suddenly struck by the thought that maybe I should be praying to recognize what is now for me. Tomorrow, the future...sure it's necessary to think about. Our familiar worlds may have changed, but that doesn't mean our personal and financial responsibilities have. Sure, tomorrow is a new day, but I find more worries flow when my mind gets stuck in tomorrow. What would change for you if you stayed in the now?

I don't know what is going to happen to my practice in a few months, but I know that right now, I have patients who count on me. I don't know what effect isolation is going to have on toddlers in 5 years, but I do know the one in front of me wants to be seen, heard, and loved. I don't know if my family and friends will be spared from the harms of the world, but I know they are here to receive love and kindness from me today.

I changed my prayer to, "What is right now for me? Help me recognize what is important for me right now."

What are you grateful for...what are you capable of...who do you need to reach out to...what do you need to do to fill yourself up or empty yourself out... what do you need to disconnect from or reconnect to...not tomorrow but right now?

Mindfully BE with yourself and others this week. Catch yourself getting ahead of yourself and stop. Look around. Choose a person (or call a person) to be with for 10-15 minutes, without distraction, instead of choosing to worry. Talk about what you are grateful for today.

Week 15

I know how to breathe.

When we are suddenly given a lot of time, we spend time wondering how to fill it.

The pandemic sent many of us home. In my family, it took about 6 weeks for us to stop struggling for air. Between telework, virtual school, and duties of the home, I could barely grasp a second for self-care even though on paper there seemed to be so much time. I think I was close to hyperventilating or holding my breath for a couple of weeks. Have you ever noticed that your breathing has just stalled?

Eventually, we were able to find a rhythm in uncertainty and loss of control and realize we were given a gift. And we found ourselves breathing again. We gave up the hold, the stall, the shallowness. We took a deep breath.

Breath is a basic building block of life. Trust yourself. You were born to breathe.

Green is the color of the heart chakra, *anahata* (the fourth chakra). It represents compassion and love for yourself and others. Take a walk outside and find a tree with beautiful green leaves (after all, it's springtime). Have a seat next to it. Take some deep breaths and notice the color of life.

Week 16

Today is/was a good day.

Even tiny negative thoughts can make us lose our perspective; these thoughts prevent us from receiving each day—each 24 hours—as a gift. For example, common thoughts like these can ruin our day: It's going to be a bad day because it's raining, or because we are short-staffed at work, or because I didn't leave room for the unexpected in my schedule.

We can also keep ourselves in the game with simple thoughts. We could choose to ask ourselves, "What if the weather doesn't affect our day? What if we practice good teamwork? What if the day goes off without a hitch?"

Let the day be what it is. Give others space to be. Keep yourself in the game. It will be a good day.

Diffuse a combination of orange and lemon oil each morning this week as you get ready for your day. These essential oils provide energy and positivity to keep you in the game of having a good day.

Week 17

I am in good company.

Isolation has certainly wreaked some havoc, but it has also opened up much needed space for many folks to turn inward…towards themselves or even to family…and begin processes of growth and healing.

People who are in a household of one are realizing they aren't so bad to be with. People who were always so busy are home, and time has opened up for storytelling and laughter. People who filled their time with social engagements to avoid themselves or to avoid quiet are realizing they need to re-evaluate the company they keep once they can keep company again.

Consider creating a life that leaves you saying each day, "I am in good company."

Start in downward facing dog. Step your feet forward toward your hands. Feel the 4 corners of your feet in the ground (2 at your heel, 1 at your big toe mound and 1 at your pinky toe mound). Press into the ground and slowly rise to standing, reaching your arms up over your head, spreading your fingers wide. Look up to the sky. This is *extended mountain pose,* a form of tadasana. This pose makes me feel like saying, "Hello, world!"

Week 18

I release my grip.

I release my grip.

Deep breath.

I release my grip.

What are you still holding onto? What were your expectations of yourself for the past year? Mine were the following: grow my practice, have a bigger presence on social media, write more, foster a creative learning environment for my son, maintain a peaceful and loving relationship with my husband, get a volunteer-based free yoga program for people living with Multiple Sclerosis online, perform self-care (because adult coloring books always sound so relaxing), keep the house clean, join Zoom meetings with friends and colleagues weekly, take all the supplements and make all the food to stay healthy, join all the things to stay involved, and sleep.

My God, I'm exhausted just reading all of that!

Even more exhausting was the act of calling myself a failure for not launching a blog during the pandemic, a failure for not restructuring my practice during the pandemic, a failure for not coloring every night during the pandemic, for not finding a job on the frontlines during the pandemic, for not cleaning out more closets AND the garage blah blah blah…in spite of my quite marked success of making it through each day.

The more I told myself I'd failed, the more I missed out on what was right in front of me: my son needing a non-distracted mom; my husband needing a nurturing wife; myself needing a peaceful and abundant me…and abundant doesn't mean busy.

So, I released my grip on all the extra things I'd told myself had to get done. I released my grip on not having the time for extra things. I released my grip on all I can't control.

You know that feeling you get when you hold hands with someone you love? Your palms nestle together, your fingers rest…it's like a sigh. Hold onto that. Hold onto what is most important. Release your grip on the extra.

Sit comfortably on the floor or in a chair. Squeeze your brow and your eyes. Purse your lips, and hold it for a few seconds. Inhale, and on the exhale, let your face relax. Now draw your shoulders up to your ears and hold them there for a few seconds. Inhale, and on the exhale, roll them down and back. Finally, draw your hands into fists, bend your elbows, and bring your fists towards your shoulders, squeezing your fists and bicep muscles tightly. Inhale, and on the exhale, relax your arms…and release your grip.

Week 19

I was created for this.

Are you working on a goal that is challenging? Are you facing some uncertainty in your work or your personal life? Do you find yourself saying, "I would really love *xyz* but I'm just not sure it is possible for me?"

Stop and listen to that soft, small voice in your head: You were created for this.

You were given the tools and support you need to become and overcome. You deserve.

Go to your mirror morning and night this week. Look yourself in your eyes and say, "I was created for this."

Go to your local market and buy a bunch of flowers in colors that appeal to you. Set them in a sunny place in your home. Flowers don't wonder about uncertainty. They were created, as you were, to bloom.

Week 20

I can let in more air.

Loneliness is not only a social issue, it is also a nursing diagnosis and close to becoming a medical one. So many people, quite literally, are alone. Others are surrounded by people and feel very lonely.

Loneliness can feel suffocating. The juxtaposition is that being alone, but not lonely, can provide space.

Maybe you are alone and not lonely because you are connected to a higher power or to others; or maybe you are connecting with yourself for the first time. Either of these things can cause emotions to rise to the surface that may feel suffocating at times.

Maybe you are searching for something. Searching relentlessly with hyperfocus is actually pushing, instead of allowing in. And it may feel stifling, exhausting.

I was looking at pictures from a time in my life when I took a bit of a sabbatical to search. I did so with an allowing in mentality, instead of my usual hyperfocused pushing. I did things that were unplanned, rolled down my windows, and let in more air. I was alone, but not lonely. I realized what I was most searching for was space.

Whatever journey you are on, make a commitment to take out the suffocation, the stifling, the exhaustion. Make a commitment to make space. Where in your life can you send loneliness packing because you let in more air?

Drop a few drops of ylang ylang essential oil in your diffuser. Inhale its soothing and grounding fragrance.

Week 21

I am a part of the bigger picture.

Some people are manifesting their quarantine dreams. Others are wondering how to reintegrate. What will look different for them? How long will it look different? Will anything ever be normal?

We are different people with different personalities, and we make different choices based on our interpretation of our world. I've had a chance to re-evaluate my who's, how's, and why's in the past year, and what is clear to me is this: my choices affect not only my growth and healing, but that of others.

So, whether you are still working from home or returning to the office; still doing yoga on Zoom or entering a re-opened gym...your response to other humans has a ripple effect. Remember to smile with your eyes, even if your mask is off. You are a part of the bigger picture. Create a picture that matters and moves us forward.

From tadasana, fold forward at your hips, keeping a slight bend in your knee to protect your lower back. Let gravity help your arms and head hang. This is *standing forward bend, uttanasana.* Let the weight of the day (heck, the year!) roll off your back.

Week 22

I can start conversations that matter.

When there is a collective problem, we hear of people coming together in meditation, breath, and prayer. While this collective energy certainly raises awareness and prepares us for challenges, it also causes us to sit in silence. If we sit in silence, we miss opportunities for responsible action and change. Let this mantra prepare you for a call to action that results in the noise of a little bit of work in your neighborhoods, your workplaces, your places of worship, your councils. Start conversations that create equality, that change history, that let the light seep in one person at a time. Start conversations that matter.

Practice mindful communication this week. Be in an alert-yet-relaxed posture when listening. Notice when you are triggered or feel an urge to interrupt a thought. Chances are your posture and breathing have quickly and unconsciously changed. Inhale and exhale slowly and reset your posture to continue listening. When you speak, speak from a place of sharing instead of convincing. Maintain the same alert-yet-relaxed posture when speaking—just as you did for listening.

Week 23

Grace is not an excuse; it's an invitation.

I often find myself saying, "Give yourself some grace." The phrase suggests things like taking it easy on yourself, giving yourself a break, relaxing, not trying to do so much or try so hard. And...it can quickly become an excuse. So, what is grace, really? As Justin Holcomb writes, "Grace is the love of God shown to the unlovely; the peace of God given to the restless; the unmerited favor of God." And right now, it sure seems like many of us could use some grace, especially those of us who have chosen to speak up as voices for something... and have chosen to enter into uncomfortable and honest conversations with friends and family as we struggle not to offend, but to lift each other up with education, information, and doing the next right thing.

Hopefully, all of us are trying to do this with grace. Make no mistake, grace is not an excuse to be merciless, to disengage, or to unlove. Grace is an invitation to embrace the peace, rest, and love you deserve as you fumble and stumble through finding your road on this journey. Grace is a nudge to do good and say the right thing, right THROUGH the lump in your throat, right THROUGH old thoughts and stories, right THROUGH to mercy, love, and peace, and right THROUGH fears of imperfection because you will not do it perfectly. And that's okay. Because you have grace. Let grace be a deep breath, an opportunity to tune in.

Buddha said, "There are two mistakes one can make along the road to truth; not going all the way and not starting." Go ahead and start, keep your foot on the gas, and invite in God's grace.

Grace is not an excuse; it's an invitation. This week fill up your grace cup.

Some believe the color of grace to be blue, like the color of the ocean that cleanses us. Blue is also the color associated with the throat or fifth chakra, *vishuddha*. This chakra is responsible for communication and speaking your personal truth. This week, wear something blue. Let it cover you in grace as you share your truth.

Week 24

I share from self, not self-image.

I have noticed a common theme among podcasts lately: letting go of the ego. Sharing from the heart. Checking your ego at the door and showing up with integrity and authenticity. Deepak Chopra asked listeners to consider what is coming from self versus self-image...and to practice returning to self. Brene Brown and Austin Channing Brown asked, "Will you choose to protect someone else over your own ego?"

The conversation you have with yourself to answer that question is a different type of hard conversation.

The message that keeps me grounded right now is the expectation that sharing word or deed from a loving heart makes up for not getting that word or deed right; that listening and learning is the best form of doing. As Austin Channing Brown so poignantly pointed out, "You may be a good person, but you can be a better one." That is truth. And it starts with digging deep and sharing from self, not self-image.

Place a few drops of vetiver in your diffuser this week. Vetiver invokes a sense of coming home to myself when I breathe it in. It feels like a hug, and you deserve one.

Week 25

I am already the person I wish I could be.

We are taught to visualize and manifest AND to believe the joy is in the journey, with all its twists and turns. Which one is right?

The joy is in the journey, that's true…but what if on the journey you chose to act as if there is no question you will arrive…instead of walking with trepidation, waiting for something to take you out, questioning your abilities. It means that you start to bring more gratitude into your every day. It means that you accept yourself just the way you are, just the way you show up…but it also means you show up to higher standards. You then begin to rise to those standards with less effort, less battle…more embodiment. You are the person you are visualizing.

From forward fold, with your knees slightly bent, lift halfway from your hips to a flat back. Place the palms of your hands on your thighs and gently press down to help lengthen your spine and pull your belly in. Roll your shoulders back and down. Let your neck be in line with your spine, no straining. You are here in *halfway lift, ardha uttanasana*, beginning to rise.

Week 26

I nourish myself with wonder.

Are you tired? The kind of tired that rest doesn't seem to solve, and little hits of dopamine don't seem to cure but for a few minutes. Are you disheartened or dejected? I heard the phrase "decision fatigue" this week, and it really resonated with me.

Are you worried about the world? About your family? About paying bills? About what to say and who to serve and what to read and when to watch and where to go to breathe and and and...

What brings you out of that abyss?

Let's think for a moment about wonder. When you hear the word "wonder", where does your mind go? Mine goes to chasing fireflies on a summer night when I was a little girl. To watching my son know to be kind. What is your moment? How does it sound and feel? What emotions does it cause to well up? Do you feel yourself smiling?

Nourish yourself with wonder this week. Spend at least a minute each day in stillness and quiet thinking about things that are wonder-ful to you. If you have the opportunity to do one thing that is wonderful, do just that.

Week 27

My effort matters.

St. Francis of Asissi said, "All the darkness in the world cannot extinguish the light of a single candle."

Do you wonder if you are doing enough? Maybe you took a social media break and you are home saying your prayers. Maybe you have never been on social media (good for you), and you are doing good deeds in your community. Whatever you are doing, however you are doing it, and whoever you are sharing it with, maybe you think it's not enough.

Effort beyond yourself in community, whether it be with family, work, friends, or the greater community, matters. Put your attention on something simple, yet meaningful, that needs it this week.

Get out those crayons (or another medium if that suits you better) and a piece of paper and make a card for someone you love. Send it out via snail mail and know that it mattered.

Week 28

Begun is half-done.

"Begun is half-done" was one of my stepdad's favorite sayings. As a little girl, I was too focused on getting things *all the way done* to understand. The journey of a thousand miles begins with a single step, right? I've found it difficult to imagine surmounting tasks at home and at work right now, so I've put some of them off. Yesterday, though, I just started one, knowing there was no way I would finish. And it felt good. Beginning feels good.

What can you begin this week that you have been putting off?

Lemongrass essential oil can be invigorating and stress relieving. See how you like it in your diffuser this week. Note: lemongrass can irritate mucus membranes, so don't use around babies or pets, and try a weaker dilution to start.

Week 29

I did my best today.

Do you ever try really hard and even double and triple check yourself, AND STILL MESS UP? I did that today. My son went to a camp at his school, and I read and re-read the email to make sure I packed the right things in his bag. I packed him a lunch that I knew he would like and got everything ready last night so there was no hurry and worry in the morning. Then, I got an email from the school asking if we were planning on picking him up at noon because he didn't have his nap things. I went to the email that I had reviewed at least 3 times... and found the info about napping right there where I should have read it. I also found that there were food allergies in his camp, and I had sent him with a lunchbox full of pistachios. UGH, UGH, UGH. I immediately started apologizing to my husband, who was the one home and had to run back up to school (which is less than a mile away). I kept re-reading the email, beating myself up, worrying about the tree-nut-allergic kid…and on and on and on…

And then I had to stop. I had just returned from a relaxing trip with my best friends feeling like I could breathe again, and this was sending me into the suffocating zone. I have been making and managing decisions about school for weeks and can't tell you how many emails I have read. I did my best today. I did my best today. I did my best today. And I'll try again tomorrow.

From tadasana (standing, arms extended towards the sky), bend your knees and work towards bringing your thighs parallel with the floor, keeping your weight in your heels. This is *chair pose,* also called *thunderbolt or utkatasana.* Hold for 2-3 cycles of breath as you continue to reach your arms skyward, rotating your pinky fingers inward and drawing your shoulder blades down and back. It can also be done in a chair, creating leg strength by pressing your feet into the ground. This powerful pose cultivates the stamina you need to keep doing your best.

Week 30

There is always enough time in the day.

I mean, some days it feels like there isn't enough time in the day...but if you let that run your mind, instead of, "I never have enough time," does your perspective change?

There is always enough time in the day to finish what is supposed to be finished.

Boom.

Alternate nostril breathing *(nadi shodhana pranayama)* is known to cause relaxation of body and mind. To start, find a comfortable seated position. Place your left hand on your left knee and raise your right hand to your nose as you exhale completely. Close your right nostril with your right thumb. Inhale through your left nostril. Close the left nostril with your right middle or index finger, then open the right nostril and exhale. Inhale through the right nostril. Close the right nostril with your thumb, then open the left nostril and exhale. This is one cycle. Try 3 cycles to start and increase as you get more comfortable with the breath.

Week 31

I forgive.

Man, forgiveness is such a toughie. It's also one of the greatest gifts you can give yourself. Have you ever been in a position where you need to accept an apology OR ask for forgiveness from someone you feel owes YOU an apology?

It's SO hard...but this type of forgiveness clears the emotional space. It allows you to create boundaries that come from objectivity rather than anger, allows emotional growth instead of increased toxicity, and often stops a relationship train that has gone off the rails.

Try it. And if you're not quite ready, but you need to get ready, try this mantra every day this week. It will help you exercise your forgiveness muscle.

Get outside for a walk this week. Concentrate on brilliant colors: the sky, foliage, even man-made objects. Find those colors in your everyday life.

Week 32

I am strong.

I am in the practice of speaking up for what I want and need in my life. This kind of speaking up is respectful of myself and others. It gently cuts through the guilt and shame that can often come with asking for what you want and need, particularly if you are in the practice of serving and giving.

Courage is required to speak about the needs of your soul's purpose, and it is a necessity to do so. You are gracefully strong. What can you ask for this week?

Try peppermint oil in the diffuser this week to enhance positivity.

Week 33

Silence is ok.

What do you reach for so you don't have to listen? TV, radio, a phone? Ironically, in searching for silence, you are searching for more noise, or a way to tune out instead of tune in.

Quiet often forces us to tune in...to listen to our heart, our intuition...to listen to something that may tell us difficult things to hear. Not to mention, there are so many things to tune into these days. It seems like someone is always offering up a new podcast, original TV series, or video about the latest conspiracy theory, or political controversy.

There is some FOMO (fear of missing out) involved in silence. But silence is okay. Silence is rejuvenating. Silence can be medicine for a busy, distracted, and tuned-out mind. Silence can get you back on track. Put your attention on the music that matters most, that aims to steer your ship in the right direction... that of your heart and soul.

From tadasana, extend your left leg behind you and invite a slight bend into your right knee. With your hands at your sides and palms facing forward, draw your shoulder blades down and back and puff your chest. Hinge forward at your hips and allow your left leg to come off the ground. Enjoy the silence of flight in *airplane pose*, or *dekasana.* Repeat on other side.

Week 34

I enjoy the rest stop.

Have you been interrupted?

As a young girl, I was taught to recognize that joy is in the journey; looking only forward to the destination causes lessons, love and life to be missed. Journeying, however, still involves moving. Right now, many of us are still and have literally canceled journeying. What then do we do with the space between?

There exists a restless anxiety to move toward the next thing. Whether a special event, opportunity, idea or just a closet clean-out, the recent past has left us stopping and starting, moving backwards and forwards. Do you recognize the space between the stop and the start as a rest stop, a gift?

There is a breath in yoga called Sahita Kumbhaka. Simply put, it is a pause at the top of inhalation and at the bottom of exhalation; awkward at first, then like most things, less so. When we are used to constantly moving, rest and pauses feel awkward at first, but soon become the space we crave.

Where is your favorite rest stop? Have you been there lately? Move intentionally to the pauses offered right now. They are intentional gifts.

Find a comfortable seated position. Pay attention to your breath. Take a few long, slow and deep inhales, with long, slow and complete exhales. When you are comfortable with that rhythm, inhale and hold your breath to a count of 1-3 at the top of your inhale. Exhale, and hold your breath to a count of 1-3 at the bottom of your exhale. Do this for 3-5 cycles of breath for improved concentration, anxiety, and lung capacity.

Week 35

--------------(silence)

A few weeks ago, the Monday Mantra was silence is ok…as if it was a choice you got to make. Today I tell myself, "I choose silence instead of noise, instead of distraction. I choose tuning in instead of tuning out." This week's mantra is, simply, silence. It's not a choice. For me, today, it is a necessity.

I actually wore ear plugs yesterday. I'm so embarrassed to even share this. My sweet boy had so much energy yesterday, and a temper that was associated with throwing things to go along with it. By the late afternoon, I fell off the last knot tied in my mama rope. I got so upset with myself because I've wanted nothing more than to be a mom. I am blessed and grateful every second to have a healthy child. How could I wish for quiet? I reached out to some friends and was reassured I was not alone. My son asked why I had "marshmallows" in my ears. I laughed. And left in my marshmallows.

Tuning in is hard work. Every once in a while, and especially now, we need quiet time. I read an article about depleted surge capacity in humans. That. Each day this week, enjoy the sound of silence, and the space between your ears. Let the work do you, instead of trying so hard to do the work. Drink it in. Check out so you can check back in. Quiet. Try it.

Choose colorful and fresh foods to eat this week. Enjoy the sounds of preparing them. Notice the expression on your face when you taste something delicious; notice the memory a certain food conjures up. Let your quiet mind fill with color.

Week 36

Just this.

I study and practice a form of biofeedback called HeartMath®. One of the techniques, called Quick Coherence, involves making an attempt to experience a regenerative feeling. I call that, "just this." As in, I only need this, nothing more. I picture very specific things: the way my husband looked at me at our wedding; the feeling of my son running to me with arms outstretched and pummeling into me with a huge hug; moments of laughter that have purged me of anything remotely negative; a sacred hug; a holy knowing; a gaze of connection.

What is your "just this"? See it in your mind's eye and feel it in your body. Let it overtake you while you are driving home from work, dialing in for another virtual meeting, or in need of just one more burst of energy. Just this. It's simple. And simply the best. Feed your heart with more of it this week.

Lavendar essential oil is used to reduce stress, help with sleep, and decrease pain. It is also associated with self-awareness and peace of mind. Diffuse lavender oil this week as you listen to your heart whisper.

Week 37

I won't wish the day away.

Don't pretend like you haven't said, "I can't wait for this day to be over" sometime in the past month! Have you noticed that just when it seems it can't get any worse...it does? Worse yet, even when it has gotten worse...you (gulp) still learn something valuable?

Perhaps you can recall a bad day when you learned you were hardier than you thought; made a valuable connection; or ran into someone (or something) that turned your day around Whatever it is, if wishing the day away worked, that miracle wouldn't have happened. Think about that...and don't wish the day away.

Tree pose, also called *vrikshasana,* teaches us equanimity. While it calls on stability and balance, it encourages us to wave in the wind. Stand tall with your hands at heart center, your feet slightly apart and your hands at your sides. Shift your weight to your left leg. Bend your right knee and place your pointed right foot at your left foot's inner arch, so your right heel rests on your inner left leg OR lift your right foot so the sole hugs your inner right calf. Press down through your left foot. Pull your sacrum slightly forward, pull your belly in and up, lift your sternum. Inhale as you raise your arms up over your head in a V-shape. Let your roots bring balance as your arms grow towards the sky and flow with the breeze.

Week 38

I'll let it take me where I need to be.

I got a new pair of running shoes a couple of weeks ago. I spent more money on running shoes then I have for years, back when I was training for marathons. I needed some motivation to start to pick up my mileage again and invest in some me-time (running without pushing 60 pounds of a stroller + toddler). I set out on Saturday morning for just 5 miles.

It was breezy, and I could feel fall in the air. I was smiling, and right at 1.5 miles, I felt a hot poker jab into my left butt cheek and my hamstring gave out. I nearly fell. I stopped, took a deep breath, and kept going. There I was, tears running down my cheeks, gritting my teeth, and screaming inside, "Don't let it take you out; don't let it take you out!" I turned my music louder. I made it to 4 miles after stopping several times to stretch.

In that last 30 seconds of running, a line from a song touched my soul. I released my grip on my jaw, took a deep breath, and then sighed. The tears really came then, and my inner voice said, "Don't let it take you out. Let it take you right where you need to be."

I've spent my life running, literally and figuratively. The past few months have presented me with opportunities to slow down and to figure things out without the frantic pace. Slowing down creates space for miracles and allows you to actually see them. You're right where you need to be.

Sit in a comfortable position and close your eyes gently. Start a running list of gratitude in your mind for the past week. When your list feels complete, cross your arms in front of your chest and give yourself a hug.

Week 39

Let the endlessness be an invitation.

I took a picture this morning of the ocean and the sun barely rising; I was on a barefoot beach walk. The right-hand side of the picture ends but the horizon doesn't…It is never-ending. I realized at that moment that healing begins at some point when the endlessness becomes an invitation to joy and learning and grace…Instead of an insurmountable task.

It was the anniversary of a late pregnancy loss for me, and a day when I allow myself some quiet. This morning, I thanked my angel baby, Aaron, for setting my feet on the path of healing my relationship with my body, food, and myself—a path that has had detours, painful bumps, earthquakes, and rainbows. I thanked Dane, my son, for calling to me, for being the invitation that says, You, Yes, YOU! Come explore the goodness that awaits you! It truly is endless…and it heals.

Find a picture that is full of endless color or emotion, one that pulls you right into the place where it was taken or to the scene and the people. Get pulled in. See the colors (endless!) and feel the experience (always available!). Set that picture as your desktop for the week.

Week 40

Freedom.

It's just one word. And I'm not trying to wax political right now. When you close your eyes and breathe it in, how does it feel in your body? In your bones, in your core, in your heart? What does it look like for you? Hold onto that. What do you need to let go of or change in your life to have more freedom?

I have come to the realization that I have held myself back from completely stepping into an integrative healing space because I am afraid of what my colleagues would say. So, I hang onto what is conventional because I built my professional life on a masculine reputation—head of the class, hard worker, overachiever, award winner! Guess what freedom feels like to me? Letting go of those notions; stepping into a feminine healing space;

trusting that I am not sacrificing my intellect, experience or work ethic, owning the notion that I deserve balance.

Freedom feels like balance to me. Freedom allows me to be a better person for my family and friends, and in my work. Bring more freedom into your week.

Patchouli essential oil is associated with balance, confidence in the body and a sense of childlike joy. It has a strong scent, so I recommend passing a bottle under your nose to gently inhale it.

Week 41

I let go of restlessness.

I was doing yoga outside yesterday and watching the clouds whiz by overhead. It was a bit of a marvel that I could be so still…and so content… while things moved by me so quickly. I had a quick picture in my head of grabbing onto a cloud and being jolted and jerked around as I trailed behind it, holding on for dear life, trying to fit into the cloud race. It seemed tiresome.

In the past few weeks, I have made decisions and changes that affect the direction of my professional life. I acknowledge that I am a lifelong learner. My curiosity and thirst for knowledge is a trait that I am proud to carry. A friend told me, "That's just you; you are always looking for the next thing, always learning."

Part of the quest comes from a restless feeling of "I am not yet enough." I said, "You're right. But I am giving up the restlessness." I struggled over the words as they came out, so I knew they were meaningful.

What can you let whiz by, so you can enjoy being enough right this very moment?

Sit on the floor with your legs extended straight in front of you. Place your hands by your hips, palms down on the floor, and create a straight spine. Bring weight to your sitting bones. Flex your feet towards your face, tightening your thighs and pressing out through your heels. Imagine your tailbone, an extension of your spine, roots you into the Earth. Breathe in and lift your sternum. Welcome the balanced posture of *staff pose,* or *dandasana.*

Week 42

It takes both rain and sunshine to make a rainbow.

But it feels like a lot of rain sometimes. When my thoughts get dark and stormy, I usually find my eyes on a rainbow. Quite literally, there is one right there in front of me. It completely reframes my thought pattern. Gratitude for all who have gone before me, somehow looking out for me, rushes in.

Don't get too stuck in your stew. Look up and invite in a smile.

Yes, there is actually a rainbow breathing technique! Sit comfortably and close your eyes. Take longer and slower breaths than usual. Imagine the red ribbon of rainbow being drawn in your mind's eye and feel it's warmth. Then, the orange ribbon and it's feeling of safety. Next, the yellow ribbon; let it fill you with energy. Then green fills you up with love; blue with your truth. Finally, purple with connection to the oneness of all that is greater than you. Hold the beauty of your rainbow in your mind for a few breaths, then gently open your eyes.

Week 43

It's such a relief...

Yep. This is a fill in the blank.

It's such a relief to listen to my body. To not fight my body. To say yes to play and joy. To say yes to rest. To say yes to love. To say yes when help is offered. To make good choices for my family. To wake up. To stand up for justice and denounce wrongdoing. To expect the truth. To have good work to do.

It's such a relief to _____.

Find art in your life. Take some time this week to look through old pictures of your favorite people, places, and things to do. Admire your favorite pieces of art. Your life is a creative masterpiece, an original. Find relief in the pages of its story.

Week 44

It's okay to miss a beat.

It took 43 weeks and COVID-19 in my body for me to miss a Monday Mantra. Sometimes enough is enough. And you miss a beat. Maybe you do it by accident or maybe you do it on purpose. But you loosen the reigns. You throw caution to the wind. And in being with the music of now, you miss a beat. What a beautiful song you have made.

Frankincense was not a random gift to baby Jesus from the Wise Men. This oil assists the soul in its wisdom, allows a spiritual connection, and guides along a lighted path. Diffuse in your home for discernment.

Week 45

I can't hold it in anymore.

I wrote this at the bottom of a page when I started these mantras. I didn't know when or even if it would show up. But it did…because I couldn't hold it in anymore, and the letting it out was extremely healing. When things get held in, we eventually have toddler-like tantrums…of grown-up proportions.

Instead of a tantrum, I chose to relent.

To relent means to abandon cruel treatment. To relent means to reach your hand up out of the rapids you threw yourself into and take the hand of your gentler self, the hand of your God, and the hands of all the people who love and care for you and get pulled onto shore. To let the sun warm you. To love, to forgive, to move forward without fear.

The opposite of fear is love, and I choose love.

Put some attention on what feels relentless to you. Can you feel a tantrum brewing? Can you work on a plan for relenting with love and kindness?

Legs up the wall pose, or *viparita karani*, is also called *waterfall* because of its anxiety-relieving and rejuvenating nature. Find a clear wall space. Sit on the floor as close to the wall as you can, lower down onto your back, and scoot your bottom to reach the wall. Gently lift your legs up the wall. You can place a folded blanket under your hips or move your hips away from the wall a bit if your hamstrings are tight. Close your eyes. Accept the relief.

Week 46

I can invite help into my life.

It's hard enough to ask for it. But then you have to let it in and be a good host or hostess! You have to want it to stay. Let down your guard and give up "your way."

Allowing help allows you rest. It also allows another person to help, care, and serve. It's a beautiful example of symbiosis.

Ask for help with something this week. When you receive help, be mindful of the experience. Notice your emotions from the beginning to the end of the experience, and even the rest of the day. Take a few moments at the end of the day to imagine the experience without help, and to have gratitude for the gift of it.

Week 47

My priorities have changed.

Our priorities change as we experience life. Our focus may widen or narrow. In either case, we are called to re-evaluate where we invest ourselves and our time.

What is essential to you? What are your priorities this week? Can you say yes (or no) using your heart and core values to steady you?

The color of our third eye (sixth) chakra is indigo. Our third eye, or *ajna*, right between the eyebrows, links us to our intuition and integrity. Indigo is a deep blue-violet color. Wild indigo and some hydrangeas wear the color. If you can't find those plants around you (it's winter in many places), download a picture for your screensaver this week.

Week 48

I don't have all the answers, but I'll do the best I can.

We have so many decisions to make. Sometimes we are asked to make decisions on behalf of others, while we struggle to make the "right" decisions for ourselves. Know that you have resources, use them to the best of your ability, make your decision, and let grace take the weight off your back. You don't have to have all the answers, just do the best you can.

Neroli has stabilizing qualities and encourages adaptation and acceptance in relationships. It has a lovely scent for diffusing.

Week 49

Stop. Drop. And Listen.

What do you hear? All the things in your head? The things you need to do, the way you shouldn't be talking to yourself, the anxiety of now and tomorrow, the hurt of yesterday? Stop it. Drop it. And Listen. Listen to the song in your car. Listen to the birds, the sound of the wind through the trees. (Did you know there is a word for that. Yep, it's psithurism.) Listen to the sound of shells clattering over each other as the tide pushes them, the sound of your family. Stop, drop, and listen to things that bring you joy.

Savasana, less favorably called *corpse pose,* allows you to practice the art of relaxation, of being with what is. Lay on your back, with support under your knees or under your head and upper back if you need it. Keep your arms by your sides, with your hands facing up and let your feet fall open, like the beginning of a snow angel. Close your eyes. Breathe in from your toes out through the top of your head, and then exhale the breath back through your toes. Relax your forehead, your ears, your tongue, the inside of your mouth. Relax your shoulders, your belly, your hips, your feet. Allow your eyes to cross. Just be. When you are ready to exit the pose, flutter your eyelids to gently let in light. Wiggle your fingers and your toes. Roll onto your right side and hug your knees close. You are loved.

Week 50

I can meet the goal as it is available to me today.

It's the end of the year. There is so much to do. There is so much to do that doesn't even matter, except that every year around this time it shows up on your calendar. So, you keep running on the treadmill of "I have to do that thing."

Guess what? You don't have to do that thing. At the very least, you don't have to do that thing, that way. Meeting the goal as it is available to you is better than not meeting it at all. So, if you have the energy or time for 30 minutes of self-care instead of 60, take the 30 and win the game. If you joyfully make one type of cookie instead of begrudgingly making five types, staying up until after midnight and exhausting yourself, make one and win the game. Got it? Good.

Meet your goal today mindfully. Drop the self-deprecation of "I didn't do enough" and enjoy the time you have devoted to what is important to you. Drop the expectation of how much time you wish you had. Enjoy the gift of being in the moment and working towards the goal. Remember Week 28? Begun is half done.

Week 51

I am choosing to play.

I've always been the kind of kid who did her homework first. No one told me to behave that way, it's just the way I was…and have continued to be. When I get home from work, I put all the things away and get organized before I play with my son, who has been begging me to play from the moment I walked in the door. I've been thinking about what is missing from my life, and it usually comes back to ease, play and self-care. OK not usually, ALWAYS.

Guess what? We fear that if we add in what is missing, we won't have time for the "have-to's," but we have it all wrong. The joy that comes with choosing play makes the have-to's easier…In fact, it is in inviting in play and self-care that we actually lose the have-to's. They just get done.

Take some time this week to make a collage of your favorite people, places, things, and colors. Enjoy your work, enjoy the memories, and enjoy the peace that comes from knowing all of this is available to you.

Week 52

I am enough.

Say it. Say it over and over again.

What comes up for you?

If it is a resounding, "Yes, I am!" then good for you. Keep that in your pocket.

If that "Yes, I am!" sounds like a foreign language, then it's self-doubt. "No, I'm not. I need to BE x, y, z or LOOK a, b, c or DO e, d, f to be enough."

If it's self-doubt, welcome a positive affirmation. You don't need to be, look, or do more to be uniquely you.

Here is one to try:

"I am enough. I am safe and well. I am healthy and happy and loved. I am enough."

Notice the difference in your body with that reframe. And move forward into the year from that. You are enough.

Melaleuca (also known as Tea Tree) has disinfectant properties, not just literally, but also energetically. It clears toxicity and encourages connections that foster respect, allowing one to feel empowered. Diffuse melaleuca this week to clear your space.

Thank You

A few weeks into these mantras, I wrote the words GIVING BIRTH on a note that was associated with this project. I didn't know what it meant at the time, but I do now.

I had always wanted to be a mom. I had a late pregnancy loss in my mid-30s, and by the time I reached my late 30s, single, I decided to turn that over to God. I put my faith in His idea of motherhood for me, knowing it might look different than what I wanted.

Just a few short years later, I became pregnant at the age of 40 and gave birth to a beautiful baby boy at 41. I had a joyous pregnancy. I felt healthy, connected, and in tune with all that is. I was not afraid. I trusted in His timing.

When the words GIVING BIRTH showed up in my headspace, I was a bit confused. I thought I had literally done that! But, if you were to ask me what my professional goal was in life, from a very young age I would have told you it was to write a book. In particular, it was to write a book that would help people understand that even when life looks great on the outside, there is still healing that needs to occur; that we all have work to do and help to offer each other; and that being Real (yep, like the Velveteen Rabbit) is the way to accomplish that healing. I had yet to give birth to that book.

This work represents the thoughts I have carried with me, the care I and others have given to them, the preparation I have made for their arrival, and ultimately the welcoming of them to the world that is you. Thank you for your receptivity.

A gift of this book is the intentional sequence of the yoga poses. You now have a short practice if you follow the movements in order. In addition to the mantras and other helpful modalities of self-care, the yoga practice can be completed in 10-

20 minutes, depending on the length of time you spend in each pose.

Your Yoga Practice:

Corpse Pose (savasana)

Cat-Cow (marjaryasana bitilasana)

Child's Pose (balasana)

Downward Facing Dog (adho mukha svanasana)

Extended Mountain Pose (tadasana)

Standing Forward Bend (uttanasana)

Halfway Lift (ardha uttanasana)

Chair Pose (utkatasana)

Airplane Pose (dekasana)

Tree Pose (vrikshasana)

Staff Pose (dandasana)

Waterfall (viparita karani)

Final Rest (savasana)

Jim Henson said, "Please watch out for each other, and love and forgive everybody. It's a good life. Enjoy it."

Please include yourself in the love and forgiveness.

You are enough.

Appendix

For more information on yoga poses discussed, please refer to Yoga Journal, https://www.yogajournal.com

For more information on essential oils, please refer to:

Essential Emotions (2019). Emotions & Essential Oils: A Reference Guide for Emotional Healing (7th Ed.). Pleasant Grove, UT: Essential Emotions.

Gratitude

Surrounding every human being are dozens of others who guide, lift up, reveal, praise, challenge, love and shape that human...and encourage her purpose.

I thank June H., Joe D'O., and Nancy M. for believing in this book, getting creative with publishing ideas, and when they didn't manifest, for encouraging me to forge ahead. Further, Nancy M. continued to guide me as editor, not only leaving me with her expertise but always with a greater sense of joy. Deep gratitude goes to Rob and Jill F. and Maria C. who gave blood, sweat (and maybe tears!) to the creation of the online audio, video, and web content of this book.

My friends have amazing talent. I thank Amy Lyn D'A. for her marketing and graphic design expertise; Rachel M. for saying to me at the end of 2019, "I think you should do something on social media that supports your creativity…How about "Monday Mantras with Megan?"; Michael P. for bringing "my wave" to digital life; Erin L. and Vanessa K. for helping me talk about myself; Roberta C. for reminding me that the only acceptable thing is to believe this would work. Thank you to Melissa M. for her precise and loving skill in editing the completed work and guiding me in all things related to self-publishing. We both agree that God had His hand in our meeting. Thank you to my online community for letting me know when these words were helpful and for sharing their experiences related to the mantras. I thank all of the above for their love and willingness to help. Just because they could.

Thank you to my parents (Mom, Jim in Heaven, Dad and Jackie), who have read and saved countless things I've written, been the safe keepers of boxes of journals, and who even from a young age gave me space to write for healing; to my sisters Katie and Kenzie, whose light and ambition pushes me to be a good example of the same. Thank you to my best friend, emo, my AKM, and to the ladies of the Red Tent (D, Laura, Krista, Korkki, Nix, Kristi, and Masy), who listen patiently to my ideas, and share in my growing pains and joy. Thank you to my husband, Ross, for understanding the difference between my purpose and my heart's work...and for creating space for me to do both. And finally, to our son, Dane, for giving the work behind this adventure an even greater purpose.

Thank you, God, for giving us a channel to You through prayer; for all these people (and more) who know and shape my heart and are examples of goodness; and for eyes to see beauty in our world.

Maktub.

Named one of the Great 100 Nurses of Northeast Florida, Megan Weigel is a Jacksonville Beach-based nurse practitioner specializing in wellness and disease prevention.

After leading yoga classes for people living with Multiple Sclerosis, Megan realized something bigger than traditional medicine was at work in the body's healing process. She pursued an integrative medicine fellowship at the University of Arizona and shortly after completion, started her own integrative medicine practice. She prescribes mindfulness practices as a key component of calming the nervous system and readying it for wellness.

Megan is an advocate for the importance of one's personal story, the search for meaning and the value of relationships in the healing process. She finds her own healing in the stillness of writing, in the movement of yoga, running and surfing, in travel and in service to her community.

The recipient of many accolades, including the University of Florida's "Outstanding Young Alumnus" award, Megan continues to consult and speak about wellness and MS care all over the country while enjoying her own journey with her husband and son in Jacksonville Beach, Florida.

For more information, visit her website, www.mondaymantraswithmegan.com.

@mondaymantraswithmegan

Monday Mantras with Megan

Made in the USA
Las Vegas, NV
13 September 2022

55205557R00095